Remove This Form Before Giving This Book To a Pupil

For TEACHERS ONLY

*FREE at any Sheet Music Dealer

Schaum TEACHERS GUIDE

Organized to SAVE TIME

Helps Make TEACHING EASIER

Includes:

- Musicianship Development
- Curriculum Planning
- Psychology for Success
- Effective Use of Sheet Music
- Easy-to-Use Index
  with Over 80 Helpful Categories
- Descriptions and Thematics
  from over 170 books and over 190 pieces of Sheet Music
- Listings by Level, Category, and Alphabet

Ask Your Dealer for this FREE "Schaum Teachers Guide"
(catalog of Schaum Publications, Inc.)

*Available **ONLY to TEACHERS** of Piano, Keyboard, and Organ*

* If you prefer, this catalog can be obtained by mail, *directly from the publisher* for $2.00. See instructions and questionnaire form inside back cover of this book.

to serve as an
osers. These
cy to gain an
usic has been

effectiveness
rs' experience
ano School in

ANINOFF
RT
OWSKY

SCHAUM PUBLICATIONS, INC.

10235 N. Port Washington Rd. Mequon, WI 53092

07-13
AN-20

Biographical Sketch

Frederic Chopin (SHOW-pan) is the greatest composer of music for the piano. All that had been said before him by the masters, Bach, Mozart, or Beethoven, seems, after listening to Chopin, as if written in a language foreign to the instrument. When he speaks, it is the speech of one for whom this combination of wood, wire, iron and ivory is a human harp — a harp from which the most exquisite poetry is plucked. This Polish composer is rightfully named the poet of the keyboard.

Chopin was born in a small village near Warsaw, Poland, March 1, 1809. He died in Paris, October 17, 1849. In those brief forty years, he lived an existence devoted to art, a life that literally burned away his frail frame. He never married; he never gathered riches; and the honors heaped upon him as a virtuoso, the fame that greeted him wherever he went, brought him no message of joy. He was a dreamer of dreams.

Yet it must not be imagined that he was a sentimental dawdler. He labored over his compositions, working for hours, days, weeks, and months at one piece. He gave many lessons, but saved no money. A few visits to England, a trip to the island of Majorca in the Mediterranean Sea with the Sand family, where he nearly perished of lung trouble — this about comprises the history of Chopin. His life is written mainly in his music. To it we must go to understand the man.

Index

Les Sylphides Mazurka

F. CHOPIN, Op. 33, No. 2
Arr. by John W. Schaum

Note: Les Sylphides (lay sill-FEEDS) is the title of a famous ballet based on Chopin's music.

Waltz in E Minor

F. CHOPIN *
Arr. by John W. Schaum

*This waltz has no opus number because it was published posthumously (after the death of the composer).

mf
p dolce
mf
f accel.
ff

Etude in E Major

F. CHOPIN Op. 10, No. 3
Arr. by John W. Schaum

poco
a
poco
cresc.
f
ff
f
mf
p
pp

Mazurka in B♭ Major

F. CHOPIN, Op. 7, No. 1
Arr. by John W. Schaum

Raindrop Prelude

F. CHOPIN, Op. 28, No. 15
Arr. by John W. Schaum

Nocturne in E♭ Major

F. CHOPIN, Op. 9, No. 2
Arr. by John W. Schaum

Andante cantabile

p
mp
p
pp
mp
8
sempre dim.
p
pp
8

Butterfly Etude

F. CHOPIN, Op. 25, No. 9
Arr. by John W. Schaum

p a tempo
poco a poco cresc.
f
rit.
p a tempo
mf

Prelude in A Major

F. CHOPIN, Op. 28, No. 7
Arr. by John W. Schaum

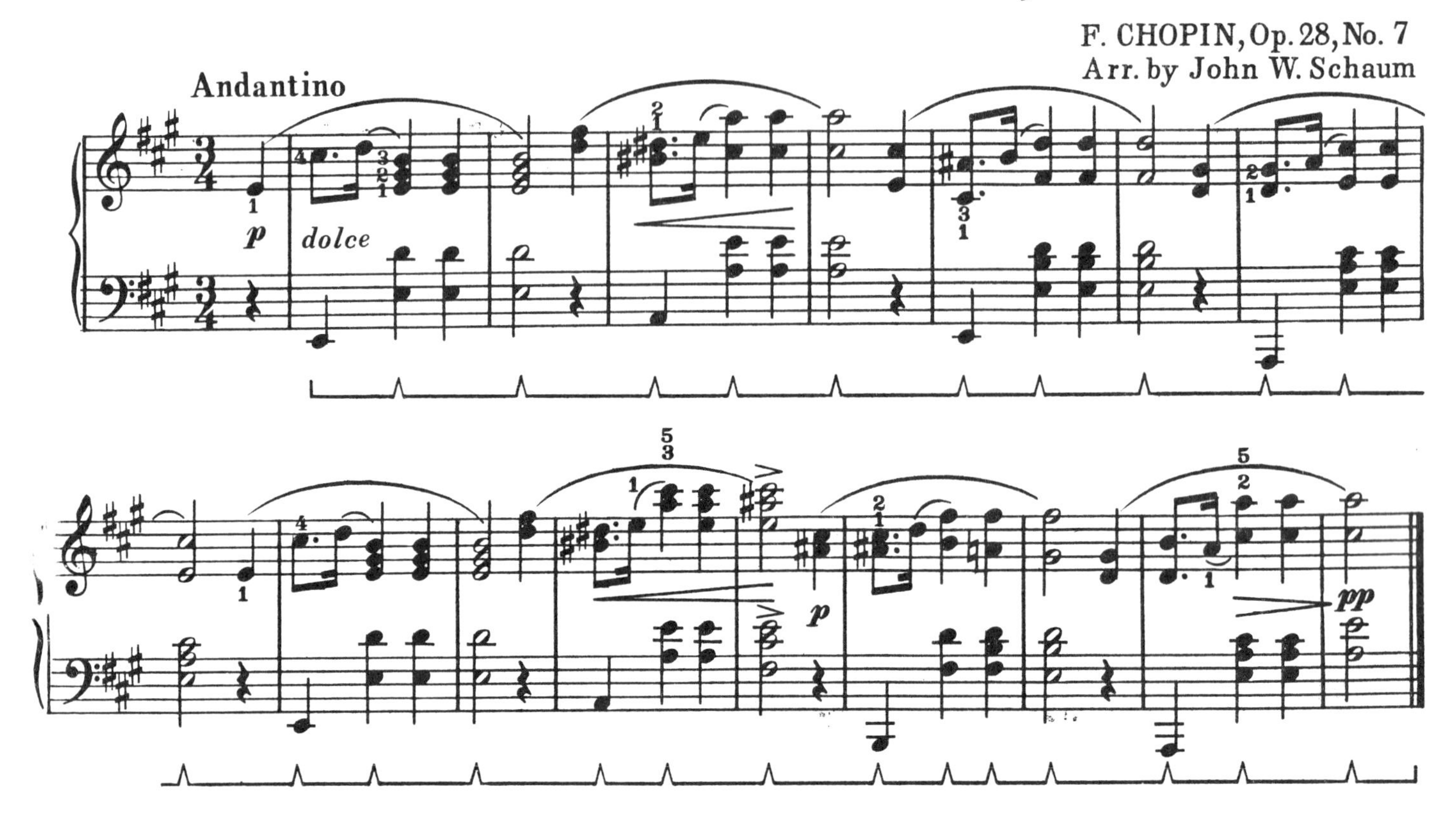

Prelude in C Minor

F. CHOPIN, Op. 28, No. 20
Arr. by John W. Schaum

Prelude in B Minor

F. CHOPIN, Op. 28, No. 6
Arr. by John W. Schaum

Polonaise Militaire

F. CHOPIN, Op. 40, No. 1
Arr. by John W. Schaum

R.H.
R.H.
mf
f

cresc. molto
ff
f
R.H.
R.H.
rit.
fz

Fantaise Impromptu

Minute Waltz

F. CHOPIN, Op. 64, No. 1
Arr. by John W. Schaum

dolce
1.
2.
rit.

Grand Polonaise

F. CHOPIN, Op. 53
Arr. by John W. Schaum

a tempo
rit.
Fine
ff
mp
p
mp
f
ff
D.C. al Fine
pesante
rit.

BEST OF BRAHMS Level 5

- 14 FAVORITES by One of the World's Most Revered Composers
- Includes Themes from CHAMBER MUSIC PIANO LITERATURE SYMPHONIES
- With Composer Sketch and Biographical Data

CONTAINS:

A Rose Breaks Into Bloom
Hungarian Dance No.5
Hungarian Dance No.6
Intermezzo, Op.117 #1
Intermezzo, Op.117 #2
Intermezzo, Op.118 #2
Liebeslieder Waltz, Op.52 #4
Lullaby, Op.49 #4
Symphony No.1 (4th Mvt. Theme)
Symphony No.3 (3rd Mvt. Theme)
Symphony No.4 (2nd Mvt. Theme)
Waltz, Op.39 #2
Waltz, Op.39 #5
Waltz, Op.39 #15

BEST OF CHOPIN Level 5

- 14 WELL-KNOWN THEMES by the Polish Composer Named the "Poet of the Keyboard"
- Selected and Arranged for EFFECTIVENESS in TEACHING
- Includes Biographical Data and Composer Portrait

CONTAINS:

Butterfly Etude
Etude in E Major
Fantasie Impromptu
Grand Polonaise
Les Sylphides Mazurka
Mazurka in Bb Major
Minute Waltz
Nocturne in Eb Major
Polonaise Militaire
Prelude in A Major
Prelude in B Minor
Prelude in C Minor
Raindrop Prelude
Waltz in E Minor

BEST OF RACHMANINOFF Level 5

- 11 MASTER THEMES by the Great Russian Romanticist
- Variety of Styles from Intimate to Bravura
- Arranged with Sensitivity

CONTAINS:

Barcarolle Op.10, No.3
Concerto No.2 (1st Mvt.) Op.18
Concerto No.2 (3rd Mvt.) Op.18
Moment Musical Op.16, No.3
Polichinelle (1st Theme) Op.3, No.4
Polichinelle (2nd Theme) Op.3, No.4
Prelude in C# Minor Op.3, No.2
Prelude in G Minor (1st Theme) Op.23, No.5
Prelude in G Minor (2nd Theme) Op.23, No.5
Serenade in B-flat Minor Op.3, No.5
Valse Op.10, No.2

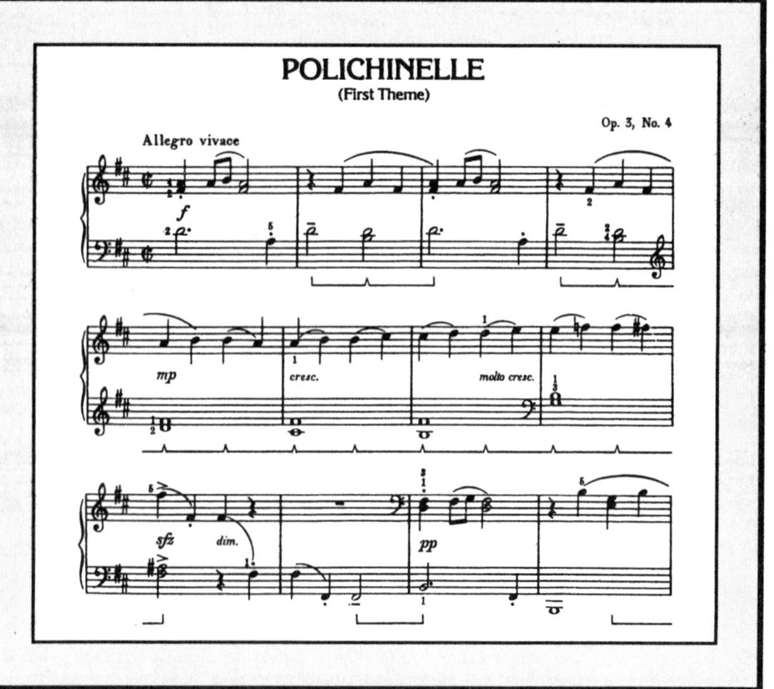